THE COMPLETE PIANO PLAYER
BEE GEES

Arranged by Kenneth Baker

Wise Publications
London/New York/Paris/Sydney/Copenhagen/Berlin/Madrid/Tokyo

Exclusive Distributors:
Music Sales Limited
8/9 Frith Street, London W1D 3JB, England.
Music Sales Pty Limited
120 Rothschild Avenue, Rosebery, NSW 2018, Australia.

Order No. AM82231
ISBN 0-7119-2462-7

Compiled by Peter Evans.
Music arranged by Kenneth Baker.
Music processed by Musicprint.
Cover photograph courtesy of Rex Features.

www.musicsales.com

Printed in the United Kingdom by
Caligraving Limited, Thetford, Norfolk.

MASSACHUSETTS

Words & Music by Barry Gibb, Robin Gibb & Maurice Gibb

C
chu - setts,
chu - setts,
mf
C♯o
the day I
they brought me
dim.
G
left her
back to
D7
stand - ing on her
see my way with
G
own.
you.
p
1.
C
D7
2.
C
They brought me
cresc.
G
back to
D7
see my way with
mf
G
you.
C♯o
They brought me
p
G
back to
D7
see my way with
G
C
you.
G
P
*

I STARTED A JOKE

Words & Music by Barry Gibb, Robin Gibb & Maurice Gibb

C
D7
2.
G
(FINE)
no.
me.
me.
Em
Bm
I looked at the skies, running my
C
G
hands o - ver my eyes. And
Bm
Em
Em7(on D)
I fell out of bed, hurt - ing my
Am7
D7sus4
D7
D.C. al FINE
head from things that I said. Till

FIRST OF MAY

Words & Music by Barry Gibb, Maurice Gibb & Robin Gibb

C Dm F C
ne-ver die, but guess who'll cry, come first of May.
dim.
mp
The
(Melody)
Em F C G7
ap-ple tree that grew for you and me, I watched the ap-ples fall-ing one by one. And
C Em F C G7
(Melody)
I re-call the mo-ment of them all, the day I kissed your cheek and you were gone.
Now
F C Dm C C7
we are tall, and Christ-mas trees are small, and you don't ask the time of day. But
mf
F C Dm G C
you and I, our love will ne-ver die, but guess who'll cry, come first of May!
dim.
rit.
mp

MORNING OF MY LIFE (IN THE MORNING)

Words & Music by Barry Alan Gibb

Am
pools of wa - ter, iced from
in a world that no one
Bm
Am
cold night, in the morn - ing,
un - der - stands, in the morn - ing,
C
mf
'tis the morn - ing of my
'tis the morn - ing of my
1.
D
life.
In the
mp
2.
D
life.
C
G
'Tis the morn - ing of my life.

NEW YORK MINING DISASTER 1941

Words & Music by Barry Gibb & Robin Gibb

F
E7
To Coda
out - side? Don't go talk - ing too loud, you'll cause a land - slide, Mis- ter
Am
Am(maj7)
Am7
Am(maj7)
VERSE
Am
Jones.
I keep strain - ing my ears to hear a
p
Am(maj7)
Am7
D7
sound. May - be some - one is dig - ging un - der - ground. Or have they
G
Am
D7
giv - en up and all gone home to bed, think - ing those who once ex - ist - ed must be
D.S. al Coda
CHORUS
CODA
G
F
dead? Have you
Am
G
F
Em
Am
Jones. dim. e rit.
p

HOW DEEP IS YOUR LOVE

Words & Music by Barry Gibb, Robin Gibb & Maurice Gibb

E♭7
Am
C11
CHORUS
soft - ly leave, and it's me you need __ to show. ___
real - ly do, and it's me you need __ to show, ___ How
F
B♭
deep is your love? ___ How deep is your love? I real - ly mean __ to
B♭m
F
Cm
learn, ___ 'cause we're liv - ing in a world of fools, break - ing us
D7
Gm
Gm-5
down, when they all should let us be. We be - long to you and
play 3 times
F
Am7
B♭
C7
Fmaj7
me.

WORLD

Words & Music by Barry Gibb, Robin Gibb & Maurice Gibb

Dm
Am
F
Em
be? To - mor - row, how far am I a - ble to
mf
mp
B♭
F
E♭
see? Or am I need - ed here?
D.C. al Coda
CODA
F
C
Dm7
C
E7
day.
And
Am
Am7
D7
Bm
Bm7
Em
now I've found that the world is round, and of
(sim)
Am
Am7
D7
C
G
Am7
G
E7
(Repeat and Fade)
course it rains ev - 'ry day. And

RUN TO ME

Words & Music by Barry Gibb, Maurice Gibb & Robin Gibb

CHORUS
G
Bm
C
Run to me when-ev - er you're lone - ly,
(me.)
run to me if
mf
Cm
G
G7
E7
you need a shoul - der,
now and then you'll
need some-one old - er, so
Cm
D7
1.
G
(VERSE)
2.
G
dar - ling,
you run to
me. And when you're
mp
Run to me when-
(me.)
f
Bm
C
Cm
G
G7
ev - er you're lone - ly,
run to me, if
you need a shoulder
now and then you'll
E7
Cm
D7
G
need some-one old - er, so
dar - ling,
you run to
me.

I'VE GOT TO GET A MESSAGE TO YOU

Words & Music by Barry Gibb, Robin Gibb & Maurice Gibb

F G C F Cmaj7
on, hold on. One more hour, and my life will be through,
Dm F G C F
hold on, hold on.
VERSE 2
Bb Cm F7
I told him I'm in no hur - ry, but if I broke her heart, then won't you
mp
Bb Cm
tell her I'm sor - ry, and for once in my life I'm a - lone, and I
D.S. (Repeat CHORUS and Fade)
F7 G7
got - ta let her know, just in time be - fore I go. I've just

YOU WIN AGAIN

Words & Music by Barry Gibb, Robin Gibb & Maurice Gibb

F
C
B♭
girl,
Oh,
girl.
Oh,
F
Em
ba - by, I'll shake you from now on.
I'm gon-na
Am
Em
break down your de - fen-ces, one by one.
I'm gon-na
Am
D7
hit you from all sides, lay your fort-ress o - pen wide.
cresc.
D.S. (Repeat CHORUS and Fade)
G
F
G
G7
No-bo-dy stops this bo-dy from ta - kin' you. So ba-by don't
f

TO LOVE SOMEBODY

Words & Music by Barry Gibb & Robin Gibb

C
G
F
to do each and ev-'ry lit-tle
thing.
But what does it
I live and I breath_for
you.
What good does it
G
D7
C7
bring
if it ain't got
you,
ain't got
you.
do,
if I ain't got
you,
ain't got
you.
CHORUS
G
D7
C
You don't know_what it's like,
ba-by,
you don't know_what it's like
f
G
D7
C
to love some-bo-dy,
to love some-bo-dy,
the way_I
1.
G
2.
G
C
G
love you.
In my
mp
love you.

HOW CAN YOU MEND A BROKEN HEART

Words & Music by Barry Gibb & Robin Gibb

Gm7
C7
How can you stop the rain from fall-ing down? How can you stop
Gm
C7
Gm7
C7
Fmaj7 F7 F6
the sun from shin-ing? What makes the world go 'round?
Fmaj7
Gm7
How can you mend this broken man? How can a lo-ser ev-er
C7
Gm
C7
win? Please help me mend my bro-ken heart,
Gm7
C7
1.
2.
F
F
and let me live a-gain. gain.

WORDS

Words & Music by Barry Gibb, Robin Gibb & Maurice Gibb

G
A
now, there'll be no oth - er time, and I can show you how, my
mp
D7
2.
Bb
Bb+
Gm
Gmsus2
love.
think that I don't ev - en mean a sin - gle word I
mf
Am7
D7
G
D7
say, it's on - ly words, and words are all I have to take your heart a -
f
mp
G
D7sus4
D7
G
way. It's on - ly words, and words are all I
D7sus4
D7
C
G
have to take your heart a - way.
rit.
mf
*

TOO MUCH HEAVEN

Words & Music by Barry Gibb, Robin Gibb & Maurice Gibb

Cmaj7
love you so much more than my life.
tears we had to cry. You're my life
I can see be-yond for ev - er,
I can see a new to - mor-row,
F
G7(on F)
ev - 'ry - thing we are will ne - ver die.
Lov - ing's such a beau - ti - ful thing.
Em7
Am
G11
dim.
Oh, you make my world a
When you are to me the
G13
sum - mer day, are you just a dream to fade a - way?
light a - bove, there for all to see our pre - cious love.
Cmaj7
Em7
Fmaj7
mp
No - bo - dy gets to much hea - ven no more, it's as high as a moun - tain, and

C G7 Cmaj7
hard - er to climb, oh, oh,
F G7 Em7
lov - ing's such a beau - ti - ful thing. You
G11
make my world a sum - mer day, are you just a dream to fade
cresc.
B♭7sus4 E♭maj7
a - way?
No - bo - dy gets too much
No - bo - dy gets too much
Gm7 A♭maj7 E♭ B♭7 (Repeat and Fade)
hea - ven no more, it's much hard - er to come by, I'm wait - ing in line.
love a - ny more, it's as high as a moun - tain, and hard - er to climb.

MORE THAN A WOMAN

Words & Music by Barry Gibb, Robin Gibb & Maurice Gibb.

Ab
Bb
Eb
Cm
Here in your arms I found my pa-ra-dise,
This is the on-ly way that we should fly,
my on-ly chance for hap-pi-ness.
This is the on-ly way to go.
Gm
And if I lose you now, I think I would die.
And if I lose your love, I know I would die.
Oh
Dbmaj7
say you'll al-ways be my ba-by, we can make it shine.
We can take for-ev-er, just a minute at a time.
cresc.
C7sus4
Oh,
CHORUS
More than a wo-man,
more than a wo-man to me.
Bbm
mf
f

D♭maj7
More than a wo - man,
A♭
more than a wo-man to me.
B♭m
D♭maj7
C7sus4
Oh!
CHORUS
D♭maj7
More than a wo - man,
A♭
B♭m
more than a wo-man to me.
D♭maj7
More than a wo - man,
A♭
B♭m
more than a wo-man to me.
A♭

IF I CAN'T HAVE YOU

Words & Music by Barry Gibb, Maurice Gibb & Robin Gibb

Gm Bb C7
Go cra - zy is what I will do. If I can't have you,
f
CHORUS
Dm C Am Dm
I don't want no-bo-dy, ba-by, if I can't have you, ah, ah! If I
C Am Dm D.S. al Coda
can't have you, I don't want no-bo-dy, ba-by, if I can't have you, ah, ah! Can't let
CODA
F C Bb Gm
- si - ly to you, my love, to dreams that ne-ver will come true. Am I strong
Bb Gm Bb C7 D.S.S. and Fade
e-nough to see it through? Go cra - zy is what I will do. If I can't have you
cresc.
f

TRAGEDY

Words & Music by Barry Gibb, Robin Gibb & Maurice Gibb

G
cresc.
just can't make it, all a - lone, I real - ly should be
just can't take it, all a - lone, I real - ly should be
F
Ab
hold - ing you, hold - ing you, lov - ing you,
hold - ing you, hold - ing you, lov - ing you,
mf
f
lov - ing you.
lov - ing you.
CHORUS
Cm
Tra - ge - dy, when the
ff
mf
Gm
Cm
Gm
feel - ing's gone and you can't go on, it's tra - ge - dy. When the morn - ing cries, and you don't know why, it's
(Repeat CHORUS and Fade for ending)
Fm
Cm
Ab
G
hard to bear, with no-one to love you, you're go - in' no - where.
cresc.

JIVE TALKIN'

Words & Music by Barry Gibb, Robin Gibb & Maurice Gibb

Am
G
F
Bbmaj7
Bm7-5
Oh, my child, you got so much, you're gon-na take a-way my e-ner-gy with all your
There you go with your fan-cy lies, leav-in' me look-in' like a dumb-struck fool, with all your
Cm
Bb
F
F(on G)
C
jive talk-in', you're tell-in' me lies, yeah! Good lov-in', still gets in my eyes.
jive talk-in', you're tell-in' me lies, yeah! Jive talk-in', you wear a dis-guise.
F
C
No-bo-dy, be-lieves what you say, it's just your jive talk-in' that gets in the way.
Jive talk-in', so mis un-der-stood, yeah! Jive talk-in', you just ain't no good.
Bb
C
C
Bb
(Repeat and Fade)

LOVE SO RIGHT

Words & Music by Barry Gibb, Robin Gibb & Maurice Gibb

Gm7
C7
A7
Dm7
Gm7
morn-ing when I woke up, I was here and she was gone, now I'm hang-ing on.
cresc.
C7
CHORUS
Bbmaj7
Am7
Dm
May-be you can tell me how a love so right can turn out to be so
mf
Gm7
C7sus4
C7
Bbmaj7
Am7
wrong. Oh, my dar-ling, how a love so right can
Dm
Gm7
C7sus4
VERSE 2
turn out to be so wrong.
f
p
Where
(Melody)
Fmaj7
Bb
Dm
did she go, when I need her close to me? And the

Am Gm7 Fmaj7 F#o C7sus4 C7
perfect story ended at the start. I thought you came forever, and you
cresc.
A7 Dm Gm7 C7sus4 C7
(Melody)
came to break my heart, now I'm hanging on. Maybe you can tell me how a
CHORUS
Bbmaj7 Am7 Dm Gm7
love so right can turn out to be so wrong. Oh, my
mf
C7sus4 C7 Bbmaj7 Am7 Dm
darling, how a love so right can turn out to be so
Gm7 C7sus4 C7
INTERLUDE
Bb
wrong, oh, my darling, I could take it in my stride, start
f
mf

B♭m6
Am7
D7
liv - ing for the mo-ment,
may - be half the things we sought were
ne - ver there.
Sim - ply
Gm7
C7sus4
o - pen up our eyes,
and
break it down to size,
it
is - n't real - ly fair
CHORUS
C7
B♭maj7
Am7
Dm
how a
love so right
can
turn out to be
so
Gm7
C7sus4
C7
B♭maj7
Am7
wrong,
oh, my
dar - ling,
how
a
love
so
right
can
Dm
Gm7
C7sus4
C7
(Repeat and Fade)
turn out to be
so
wrong,
oh my
dar - ling,
how
a

NIGHT FEVER

Words & Music by Barry Gibb, Robin Gibb & Maurice Gibb

Am
B♭
Am
sweet ci - ty wo - man she moves through the light, con - trol - ling my mind and my soul.
Em
Am
Dm
A
When you reach out for me, yeah! And the feel - in' is bright, then I get
cresc.
CHORUS
Dm
Gm
Fmaj7
night fe - ver, night fe - ver. We know how to do it.
f
Gm7
Dm
Gm
Gim-me that night fe - ver, night fe - ver. We know how to show
Fmaj7
Gm7
INTERLUDE
G
it.
Here I am,
mp

Printed and bound in Great Britain by
Caligraving Limited Thetford Norfolk

9/02 (45309)